Keeping

Stick Insects

Dorothy Floyd

Illustrations by Jason Davis
Photographs by Dorothy Floyd

Dedicated to Pritt

PREFACE

I run a company which manufactures biological equipment and breeds insects. Part of my time is spent touring the country encouraging schools and private individuals to keep stick insects. I show people different sorts of stick insects and explain how to look after them properly. The response is enthusiastic and many wide-ranging questions are asked. I have directed the contents of this book to answer these questions. For example, practical tips on keeping stick insects are given and there is a chapter covering the basic biology of these insects. I believe this book will be invaluable to anyone who has stick insects and I hope it will encourage other people to start their own collections.

Dorothy Floyd.

British Library Cataloguing-in-Publication Data available.
First published in 1987.
copyright 1987 Dorothy Floyd.

ISBN 0 9512466 0 7

Printed in Great Britain by Deanprint Ltd, Cheadle Heath, Cheshire.

Contents

chapter 1

Why keep stick insects?

What kind of creature

—grows by climbing out of its skin?

—is sometimes mistaken for a stick or twig?

—lays hundreds of eggs which can be catapulted, buried, or glued?

—may fly using its brightly coloured, patterned wings?

—is able to cling even to the underside of surfaces using the claws and suction pads on its feet?

—when alarmed can release a defensive odour or liquid?

Answer: STICK INSECTS!

Are stick insects easy to observe?

Answer: Yes! It is very easy to look at stick insects because they are so large; some adults are 20cm long and weigh 15g! By observing stick insects much can be found out about insects in general. Their large size means that details such as their compound eyes, foot structure and mouthparts can be seen easily. Many projects can be done on stick insects and some are suggested in chapter 5. Stick insects are harmless and do not bite or sting. This means that they can be handled without fear. They readily walk across one's hands and this can provide much enjoyment. There are many types of stick insect and it is exciting to collect several varieties because each one is quite different both in appearance and behaviour. Nature photographers can record the whole insect or else effect a dramatic close-up, for example of the insect's head.

Are stick insects easy to keep?

Answer: Yes! They are clean animals and a growing number of people now keep them as pets or as a hobby. The hardier types are ideal for schools. As well as being popular with the children, the stick insects have great educational value. They should be kept indoors, in a well-ventilated cage. It costs nothing to feed these creatures because they eat leaves which can be gathered from gardens or wild places. The upkeep is minimal, consisting of a weekly 'clean out' of cage and change of foodplant.

Stick insects live for about one year. They breed easily; the next generation start to appear just before the original insects die. This means that a stock of insects can be maintained continuously over several years if desired. Having been successful at keeping one sort, other varieties may be added to make a diverse collection. Seven types, all of which are easy to keep, are discussed in this book.

chapter 2

Basic biology of stick insects

1. CLASSIFICATION

Creatures which are called INSECTS all have the same basic structure when adult—six legs, two antennae, and a body which can be divided into HEAD, THORAX and ABDOMEN. These parts are labelled on the illustration below, of an adult Indian stick insect. Insects do not have an internal skeleton; instead their shape is determined by their outer skin which is called the CUTICLE.

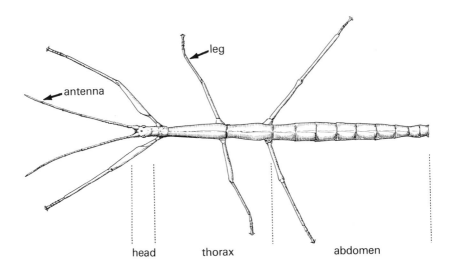

leg

antenna

head   thorax   abdomen

fig 1

Although all insects share this fundamental design, many variations have been developed over the 325 million years in which insects have existed on Earth. This is why the insects of today are such a variety of shapes, sizes, and colours. Wings are an optional feature; some insects having none but others possessing two or four wings. Stick insects are either wingless or they have two wings.

Insects which share roughly the same characteristics are assigned to an ORDER. Butterflies and moths belong to the order Lepidoptera, beetles to Coleoptera, and stick insects to Phasmida.

Within an order, insects which look identical (allowing for differences between males and females) can be put into another set or SPECIES. Breeding is only possible between insects from the same species. Of course, individuals from the same species show some variation; for example there are slight differences in colour, size, and behaviour.

2. BASIC FUNCTIONS

(a) Breathing

Stick insects do not have lungs. Instead they breathe by letting air drift into and out of their bodies. The air enters the insect through small, round, adjustable openings, called SPIRACLES. Each insect has twenty spiracles and these are spaced regularly down each side of the body.

Inside the insect, each spiracle connects with a tube. This branches into thinner tubes and these divide further and further in the same way. The smallest tubes are called TRACHEOLES and these penetrate all areas which need oxygen. This extensive network of tubes means that air can pass directly from the outside world to the tissues within the insect. Such a simple system excludes the need for special molecules to transport oxygen and this is why insects' blood does not carry oxygen.

The oxygen released by the tracheoles is then used to generate energy by the chemical process called RESPIRATION. Carbon dioxide is the waste product and this is breathed out through the spiracles. The brain detects the levels of this gas and the insect responds by closing and opening different spiracles enabling breathing in and breathing out to occur.

All the breathing tubes except the tracheoles are shed at each skin-change. After a moult, the new breathing tubes are joined to the old tracheoles by a special glue. If the discarded skin is examined, the larger tubes can be seen as glistening white threads which are much finer than the antennae.

(b) Perceiving surroundings

Stick insects gather information about the surrounding environment by using their antennae and eyes.

The antennae are covered with thousands of very small sensory hairs. These hairs are of different types, each sort being specialized in what it can detect. For example, one type can identify a particular chemical by 'smelling' it. Another sort of hair is able to register changes in the surrounding temperature. Many other hairs are involved in providing signals which help the insect to maintain its balance.

This wide range of information is relayed to the nervous system of the insect so that appropriate action can be taken.

Since the antennae provide so much information it is important that they are looked after. A stick insect can sometimes be seen cleaning its antennae—they are the only parts of the insect's body which have this treatment. If two stick insects fight, each one attempts to snap off part of the other's antennae. Weaker insects often have broken antennae and these cannot be repaired. It is not totally disastrous if antennae are damaged because the sensory hairs, although concentrated there, are present all over the insect's body. Also, of course, the sight of the insect is unaffected by this injury.

A stick insect has two COMPOUND eyes, one on either side of its head. They are called 'compound' eyes because they consist of hundreds of hexagonal lenses. All of these contribute to produce a picture of the surroundings. Stick insects see objects clearly and in colour.

In addition, some stick insects have three SIMPLE eyes and these are on top of the head. They do not form a picture—instead they register the surrounding brightness and adjust the sensitivity of the compound eyes.

(c) Moving

All stick insects walk, some such as the Pink winged variety can fly, and Javanese stick insects can jump.

When a stick insect walks, it sways from side to side, probably imitating a twig blowing in the wind. The six legs are moved in a definite sequence and this can be demonstrated by following the method given in chapter 5. Even though each leg is moved separately, the stick insect still manages to keep its balance. This is because the sensory hairs all over its body provide signals which help the insect to co-ordinate its movements. The insect acts on these signals at once and this can be especially important if the insect is injured. If a moving insect is hurt and loses one or more legs, it immediately compensates for the loss by altering the pattern in which the remaining legs are moved, and continues walking almost as though nothing had happened.

A stick insect can travel across, up, and underneath most objects. (This ability to 'stick' to surfaces has led many people to believe, mistakenly, that this is the reason why these insects are called *stick* insects. In fact they have this name because they resemble sticks or twigs.) A stick insect can hold onto such a variety of different textured surfaces because of the structure of its feet; on each foot there are two claws and four suction pads. When large insects are resting on the side of the cage their claws can be seen curved round the outside of the mesh. The foot structure can be looked at more closely if a discarded skin from a big insect is examined. When touched, the suction pads still feel sticky and the claws sharp. Unlike the rest of the skin, the claws are black because they are made from a stronger substance.

(d) Eating

Stick insects eat certain varieties of leaves. In the centre pages of this book there is a photo of a stick insect feeding and this shows its MOUTHPARTS. The long, thin, jointed structures at the bottom are the PALPS—each insect has two MAXILLARY PALPS and two LABIAL PALPS. There are many sensory hairs on the palps and these can detect whether or not a leaf is suitable to eat simply by touching it. However, although these palps can test if a leaf is of a poisonous variety they are not able to detect if a leaf has been sprayed with insecticide. Therefore it is important not to feed the insects with leaves collected from areas which might have been sprayed with chemicals. This is particularly relevant to the Corsican stick insect which eats rose leaves.

Unlike caterpillars which eat leaves continuously, stick insects have distinct meals both during the day and at night. An insect which is ready to feed will first of all brush the surface of the leaf with its palps. If it decides that it is suitable to eat, the insect positions itself at the side of the leaf. Between the head and the thorax of the insect there is an extendable 'neck' and this is softer and lighter in colour than the rest of the body. This neck enables the insect to alter the position of its head without moving the rest of its body. The insect starts feeding with its head tilted upwards. A small bite is taken out of the leaf using two sharp cutting instruments called the MANDIBLES. These make up the central region of the mouthparts. The piece of leaf is immediately chewed and swallowed. Quickly, the insect proceeds to make further bites, and chews its way down the leaf. However, this movement is not in a straight line; instead it is more semi-circular. When the edge of a leaf is reached, the insect pauses for a moment and then raises its head back to the starting position. The above process is then repeated several times and this results in the overall bite made in the leaf being enlarged. Throughout feeding, the palps are continually monitoring the suitability of the leaf.

A stick insect can only produce one kind of waste matter. This is called uric acid and is released in the form of droppings which are relatively dry and odourless.

(e) Defence

In general, animals have two types of defence, 'passive' and 'active'. A passive defence is one in which the animal hides from the enemy, for example by blending in with the background. An active defence is one in which the animal deliberately moves; this may involve running away or retaliating. Stick insects show both passive and active defences.

Their passive defence is that of camouflage. The eggs are usually grey or brown in colour so that in the wild, they blend in with the ground litter. Usually the body of the stick insect is shaped, coloured, and even textured to resemble a twig. Some insects, for example the Thailand variety, have extra small growths extending from the head or leg which makes the illusion more convincing. Other varieties resemble dry leaves. For example, the Macleays Spectre stick insect can look like a curled up dead leaf. The behaviour of the insect is adapted to keep up the pretence of being a twig. Sometimes the insect will rest on the main stem of the foodplant, jutting out at a similar angle to the real twigs. If there is a slight breeze, the insect will rock from side to side, again mimicking the plant.

There are several active defences; the one used depends on the age of the stick insect, its species, and how threatened the insect feels. Chapter 4 covers the different species of stick insect in more detail and it is in this section that their defence mechanisms are discussed. As a summary, here is a list of their possible reactions; fall to ground as stick, release fluid from mouth, emit defensive odour, show warning colouration, flash wings, release green blood from knee-joint, throw a healthy leg at enemy, hiss, stab intruder with spines.

3. LIFE CYCLE
(i) Growing

A stick insect egg usually hatches at night. The newly emerged insect can look rather comical because it has long legs and a very short body. However, within a few hours, the body has expanded, bringing the insect into proportion. The baby insect looks like a miniature version of the adult and is called a NYMPH. However it is not an exact scaled-down model — for example in winged species the nymph does not have wings whereas the adult does.

The nymph passes through several stages before becoming an adult after about five months. At all stages the nymph shows some resemblance to the adult and this type of development is called INCOMPLETE METAMORPHOSIS. This is quite different from the way some other insects grow, in which the young look totally different from the adults. For example, in Lepidoptera, the caterpillar (the LARVA) has a completely different appearance from that of the butterfly into which it develops. This type of growth is called COMPLETE METAMORPHOSIS.

A recently hatched stick insect is in its first stage of growth and this is called the FIRST INSTAR. Sometimes this nymph may retain its eggshell on one or more of its legs. The eggshell is not a food source and does not appear to be of any use to the insect once hatching has occurred. Indeed the nymph will try to discard it by trapping it on the edge of a leaf. Usually the insect is successful and the eggshell drops off.

Although some first instar nymphs die, many live and, about two weeks after hatching, enter their second instar. They do this by climbing out of their skins, almost doubling in size in the process. This moulting, called ECDYSIS, occurs several times; for example each Indian stick insect changes its skin six times. It is only the nymphs and not the adults that undergo this process.

An insect approaching the time for a skin-change will not eat for a day or two. The nymph will appear fatter than usual and, if possible should not be disturbed at this time. It is obvious when moulting is imminent because the insect selects a position, usually vertical, high up in the cage. The nymph rests here, upside-down, for many minutes.

The head is then tilted forwards and moulting begins; see **fig. 2**. The insect swallows air causing the thorax to swell (diag 1). There is a weakened line of cuticle running down the top surface of the insect from its head to its thorax and the old skin splits down this line. The new head is pulled out first (diag 2). The insect continues to slide downwards out of its old skin. If the insect has short antennae then this is the time the new ones are released (diag 3). It is usually the middle legs which are the first limbs to be pulled out of the skin. These are quickly followed by the back legs (diag 4). Shortly afterwards, the front legs are freed. For insects with long antennae, this is when the new ones appear (diag 5). The insect now pauses, suspended from its old skin by the tip of its abdomen. The old inner breathing tubes can now be seen dangling from the skin as white threads (diag 6).

The purpose of hanging like this is probably to allow the cuticle time to toughen slightly. When new it is quite soft and bright in colour, but on contact with the air it begins to harden and darken.

This process takes many hours but the feet are designed to harden much more quickly so that the insect can hold onto surrounding objects.

After many minutes, which can mean up to half an hour for an adult, the insect swings upwards and grips on to the object supporting the old skin. In doing this, the tip of the new abdomen slips free (diag 7). A wingless insect will then rest by its old skin, sometimes eating it. If the skin is touched or disturbed in any way, the insect will not eat it.

A skin which is not devoured can be removed and examined. Initially it is soft, white, and slightly wet. Interesting features include the slit in the thorax and the thread-like breathing tubes. In addition, the clear cuticle which covered the compound eyes can be seen as can the hard black substance which formed the strong cutting mandibles. After a few hours the old skin hardens and becomes more brittle. It is now fawn in colour although the breathing tubes are still glistening white.

The process of climbing out of a skin lasts from about five to thirty minutes, taking longer for larger insects. Obviously it is a vulnerable time and so sometimes another insect will guard the one that is moulting. Fortunately skin-changes which occur in captivity are usually successful.

Three main hormones can be involved in ecdysis and, depending on which are used, an insect remains a nymph or becomes an adult. The transition to adulthood is especially exciting for the winged species because this is the time when the insects gain their wings. Throughout the nymphal stages the wings have been developing as wingbuds on the outside of the thorax. Immediately after the final skin-change, in place of the wingbuds there are now cream wings which are tightly concertinad up. It is only when the insect is free of the old skin and is resting upright beside it that the process of pumping out the wings begins. This takes about thirty minutes and one can see the soft pale wings unfolding down the abdomen of the insect. When this is finished the

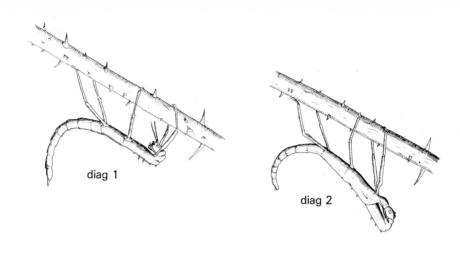

diag 1

diag 2

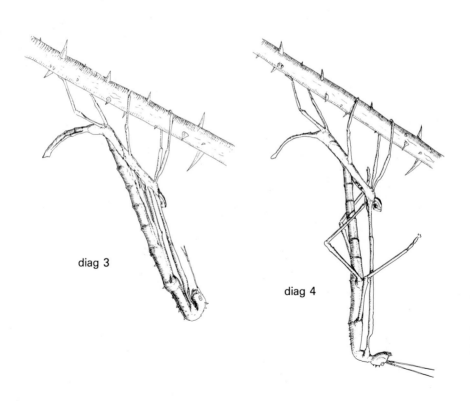

diag 3

diag 4

fig 2

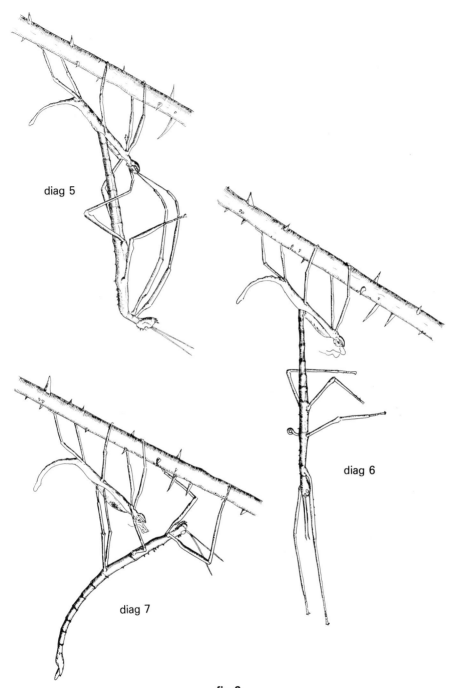

diag 5

diag 6

diag 7

fig 2

wings hang down and splay out at the bottom like a Victorian petticoat. A few hours later the insect will fold them properly across the abdomen, but it will be one or two days before the wings achieve their true colouration and longer still before they are strong enough for the insect to fly. Later on, some Pink winged stick insects develop a red spot on the thorax, between the wings. This is thought to be a warning signal.

Slight damage such as grazing can be repaired by the cuticle in-between moults.

If the damage is more serious and results in a cut being made, some blood will ooze out. The blood is green and dries on the wound thereby sealing it. The welfare of the insect is hardly affected.

Sometimes the insect receives a more serious cut and the bleeding cannot be stopped in time. If the damage is confined to one or more of the legs the insect has a chance of saving itself because it can discard the affected limb(s). There is no loss of blood at the place where the limb drops off the thorax. (The ability to lose legs is not just restricted to damaged ones. An insect can release healthy legs in an attempt to defend itself or as a means of escape.) Providing that the loss has occurred early on in the instar, a new leg can be developed and this will appear after the next ecdysis. This process is one of regrowth or REGENERATION. Initially the regenerated leg is so small that it is of little use. The insect shown in diag 6 has a middle leg which is brand new. In the course of the following moults it will increase in size and be more useful, although it will never be as large as the original legs. Of course if an adult loses a leg a new one cannot be regrown because mature insects do not shed their skins. Stick insects are able to regrow legs but are unable to regenerate antennae. So, if an antenna is completely broken off (this is very rare) a miniature *leg* is regenerated on the head of the insect at the next ecdysis! A photo of this is in the centre pages.

(ii) Reproducing

Stick insects live for about one year. During the second half of their lives they breed easily and produce many hundreds of eggs. Such large numbers of eggs are laid to increase the chances of some of the offspring surviving to adulthood — in the wild many eggs and young stick insects are eaten by predators. In captivity, this danger does not exist and so, in order to avoid becoming overrun with stick insects, it is advisable to destroy most of the eggs.

Only adult female stick insects can lay eggs. These may be catapulted, buried, or glued to surfaces — the technique depending on the species of stick insect. The eggs are not all laid at once; instead the female insect lays a few eggs each day, over a period of about seven months.

Stick insects are unusual because some species contain only females whereas others have both sexes.

Species which are exclusively female are able to lay eggs — which will later hatch to produce more females. No mating occurs and this form of reproduction is called PARTHENOGENESIS. (This is not the same as hermaphroditism. Like parthenogenetic stick insects, hermaphroditic insects from the same species are similar in appearance. However, unlike stick insects, all hermaphroditic insects possess both male and female parts and have to mate in order to produce fertile eggs.) One strange feature about parthenogenetic insects is that very occasionally male insects can occur. This has been observed in the Indian stick insect. The occurrence of these rare males is strange because they are not essential for reproduction.

The other species which contain males and females (in approximately equal numbers) reproduce SEXUALLY. A few weeks after becoming adults, the male, who is usually the smaller and more slender insect, climbs on top of the female and they mate using the genitalia situated at the tips of their abdomens. This process lasts for several hours. It does not prevent the female from walking around or even eating a leaf! The initial mating is the first of many which occur throughout the lives of the adults. No violence is shown and there is no question of the female eating the male after mating! Both sexes usually live about one year although very active insects have shorter lifespans. The stick insects have a variety of partners but these are chosen within sets; that is the stronger insects mate together leaving the weaker, perhaps damaged insects to pair off amongst themselves.

During mating, the male transfers a little bag of sperm, called a SPERMATOPHORE, to the female. He places this spermatophore on the side of the female's abdomen, near its tip. When the couple have finished mating, the bag is usually still attached to the female. It can be seen clearly in large insects such as the Macleays Spectre variety where it is white or pink in colour (see **fig 3**).

The female has an empty compartment inside the tip of her abdomen and the sperm quickly travel to this place. The sperm are stored here and they are only released when it is time to fertilise an egg. Higher up in the abdomen, nearer the thorax, the female manufactures many eggs. These pass down inside her abdomen like a production line. By the time

17

fig 3

each egg reaches the tip of her body the egg has a shell on it and appears to be finished. However, the important process, the fertilisation has yet to occur. When the egg passes by the sperm compartment, a few sperm are released in a short burst. These pass directly into the egg through a very small hole which has been left in the shell. The egg is now finished and is ready to be laid. As with parthenogenetic species, the eggs from sexual species should hatch in a few months.

An interesting situation arises for sexual stick insects if, for some reason, there is an adult female present but no adult male. Here, the adult female delays laying any eggs for several weeks. If, after this time there is still no male, the female will start to lay eggs (which are identical in appearance to those eggs produced after mating.) Although these eggs would not be expected to hatch, it has been suggested that a very small proportion do.

(iii) Egg Structure

The egg from one species of stick insect is usually quite different in colour, size, shape, and texture from that of another species (see photo in centre pages). Yet, all stick insect eggs have the same basic design (see **fig 4**).

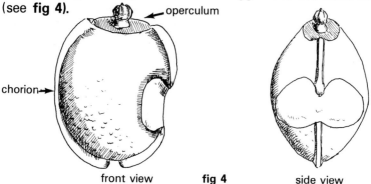

chorion⟶   ⟵operculum

front view   **fig 4**   side view

The eggshell or CHORION is made from a hard substance and this protects the inside of the egg. The external appearance of the egg does not alter during its incubation of several months. However, during this time, many changes occur inside the egg. At first, when the egg is laid, the interior is a yellow sticky fluid. Yet, within a few months, it is transformed into a stick insect tightly packed in a soft white sac. For the embryo to develop, it must maintain contact with the outside world; enabling breathing and taking in water to occur. These exchanges take place via tiny holes or MICROPYLES which are situated all over the chorion.

When the development is complete, the insect is ready to emerge. Most people are familiar with the sight of a hatching chicken smashing its eggshell and breaking it open. The egg of a stick insect is designed differently and has a special lid or OPERCULUM. The insect hatches by simply pushing this lid off with its head and pulling itself out through the opening.

chapter 3

How to look after stick insects

Like any other creature which lives in captivity, stick insects will only be healthy if they are kept in good conditions and are well cared for. This involves properly housing, feeding, and handling the insects. These practicalities are discussed in detail below.

Housing

An ideal stick insect cage is tall, well-ventilated, easy to see into, and convenient to clean out.

A tall cage, about 45cm high, is important because it gives the insects the opportunity to develop properly. Stick insects which are housed in make-shift squat containers usually become stunted or die before they are fully grown. The height is needed when the insect is undergoing a skin-change; a tall cage does not constrain the insect and provides enough room for it to slide vertically downwards out of its old skin.

The ventilation in the cage must also be correct if ecdysis is to be successful; two ventilation panels have been found to give good results.

A container with insufficient ventilation quickly becomes mouldy and smelly. The surroundings become too humid for the insects and problems may arise when they undergo skin-changes. Sometimes the old skin becomes soggy and clings to the new one. A stick insect in this state will die unless one quickly intervenes and manually removes the old skin.

A very draughty container also presents problems for insects which are trying to shed their skins. The old skin may become too dry and will not slide off the insect. The insect will die unless one immediately helps by placing droplets of water on the area where the old skin is attached; after a few seconds it can be peeled off.

Insufficient space and ventilation are reasons why containers such as fishtanks, sweetjars, and plant propagators are not suitable for stick insects.

Instead a stick insect cage can be bought—see photo of the commercially available cage in the centre pages. This cage is tall and has two ventilation panels which are made from aluminium mesh.

It is easy to see the insects in this cage because it has a clear top and front.

Access to the cage is via the clear front panel which opens as a door. A hinged door has the advantage over a sliding one in that there is less risk of trapping the insects' legs when the door is opened or closed. Siting the door at the front means that it is particularly easy to replace food and to clean the cage out. A jamjar of water containing tall sprigs of foodplant can be introduced into the cage with little risk of upset. However, if access to the cage was via the roof, the likelihood of tipping the jar over would be very great.

Cleaning the cage out involves lining the base with a sheet of paper and replacing this with a new piece. This should be done at least once a week. The old paper can be put on the table and the contents sorted. All corpses can be thrown away. Dead stick insects are usually dark in colour and have their legs crossed. Any loose leaves and shed skins can be discarded; of course first check that no living insects are mixed up with them! If eggs are present then they can now be sorted. The method by which the eggs are collected depends on the species of stick insect. Chapter 4 which describes the various species suggests the appropriate technique for each type of stick insect.

The cage should be kept indoors, in a room that is comfortably warm. A wide temperature range is tolerated; the hardier species of stick insect even withstanding freezing conditions overnight, although obviously these should be avoided whenever possible. Positioning of the cage is important; it should not be in a strong draught because the insects may become too dry and the foodplant will wither more quickly. A windowsill is not a suitable site either—the insects may then be subjected to extreme temperatures, either too hot or too cold, both of which can be lethal.

The stick insect cage which has been described holds about twenty adults. The insects usually group, sometimes overlapping each other, on the mesh. They prefer to rest here rather than on the foodplant. Different varieties can be kept in the same cage, insects from the same species tending to group together.

Feeding

Stick insects are very cheap to maintain because they eat leaves which can be gathered from outside. Most stick insects eat bramble (also called blackberry) leaves, but the Indian variety eats privet and the Javanese have rhododendron.

Bramble flourishes in places such as parks, woods, railway embankments, and the sides of canals. This food can be found throughout the year—even in severe winters plenty of green bramble leaves are present in areas which have been sheltered, for example by long grass. If the leaves have brown edges these should be trimmed with a pair of scissors. In the summer bramble-eating stick insects will also accept raspberry leaves.

Privet and rhododendron bushes are often grown in gardens. These are evergreen plants. However if there is a hard winter the privet leaves may drop off. If this happens, the stick insects can be fed with ivy leaves as these are acceptable and are always available. Some houseplants will also be eaten; the Prayer plant 'maranta tricolour' being a favourite.

The insects are only able to chew leaves which are reasonably fresh. This means that after a few days the old leaves should be thrown away and new ones placed in the cage. Rather than putting loose leaves into the cage it is better to give the insects several tall sprigs of foodplant. These keep fresh if they are stood in a jamjar of water. It is best to punch holes in the lid of the jamjar and push the sprigs through these. The lid then shields the insects from the water and prevents any young nymphs from drowning. An alternative method is to push the stems into a container holding a wet 'oasis' block. This has the added advantage of making the cage more decorative.

There should always be plenty of soft leaves in the cage—never just bare stalks (which can be gnawed but are no substitute for leaves).

Stick insects require some water in addition to the moisture which they obtain from eating the leaves. It is not wise to place a bowl of water in the cage because the insects may drown. Instead the leaves should be wetted—either by holding the sprigs under a running tap and then shaking off the excess water, or by lightly spraying the leaves with a fine mist. A scent-spray which has been cleaned and refilled with water is suitable for spraying the leaves; alternatively some fine garden sprays can be used. This process should be done every day. Some categories of insect particularly appreciate a drink; these are the newly hatched, the females that are just beginning to lay eggs and the old adults which are dying. It is easy to tell when an insect is thirsty because it wanders restlessly about the cage and vigorously exercises its mouthparts, frequently pausing to touch them against a surface.

It is not normal or acceptable for stick insects in captivity to eat each other. Fighting occasionally occurs but this usually only results in part of an antenna being snapped off. If a stick insect is actually chewed by another one the insects are not being cared for properly; they may be overcrowded or suffering from not being given enough water.

Handling

Stick insects do not bite or sting and so can be allowed to walk on one's hands. The larger insects have reasonably hard bodies which can withstand careful handling. A stick insect can be encouraged to walk across one's palm if it is gently blown on.

There is some evidence to suggest that stick insects can recognize people. For example, a stick insect which is handled every few days by one person is often reluctant to be handled by anyone else. The insect will readily walk across both palms of the person who usually handles it but is unwilling to cross over to the palm of another person. Indeed, the stick insect will often do a U-turn in order to avoid walking on the unfamiliar palm.

People who are squeamish about insects may benefit from handling a stick insect because this experience may help to dispel their fear. Experience has shown that many people sigh with relief and smile as a stick insect slowly walks across their palm, tickling slightly, and swaying from side to side.

The way in which a stick insect is handled depends on its size and species.

Picking up a very small stick insect

It is safer not to handle a newly hatched insect directly because it is so small, being only 1mm wide. Instead it can be picked up via the tip of an artist's paintbrush. The insect can be set down again either by tapping the brush or by gently blowing the insect off.

Picking up a medium-sized stick insect

The insect can be grasped around its abdomen, a short distance from the tip, and lifted. The body should never be squeezed so hard that its shape is altered.

Picking up an adult stick insect

The insect can be grasped between its second and third pairs of legs and lifted gently. Sometimes this is not possible because the insect's claws are embedded in an object. If this is the case, the insect can be encouraged to release its grip if the feet involved are touched (see **fig 5**).

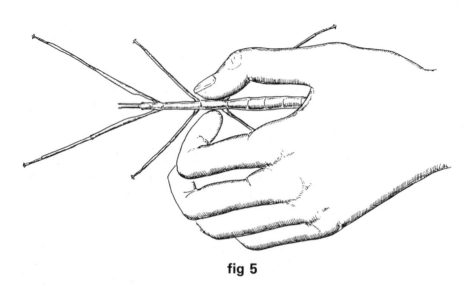

fig 5

chapter 4

Stick insects that are easy to keep

Seven species, all of which can be reared easily, are now discussed. Beginners and schools are advised to consider trying the first four species. The last three species discussed are more suited to enthusiasts.

Indian stick insects (see **fig 6**) are ideal for the beginner. They are robust, very hardy, and breed readily. These insects eat privet leaves but other plants such as ivy, bramble, and maranta are also acceptable. The colour and behaviour of the insect are affected by its diet; for example, bramble leaves appear to make the Indian stick insect more active.

This insect was brought into laboratories in Britain in the early 1900's. Since then, many physiological experiments have been done on the Indian stick insect and this is why it is sometimes called the 'laboratory stick insect'.

Eggs

A typical egg is round and 2mm long. It is smooth and brown with an orange knob on the operculum. When sorting the eggs from the droppings (frass), it is best to tilt the paper holding the mixture and tap underneath. The eggs should roll off and can be caught in a shallow dish. It is advisable not to save all the eggs because each insect lays about 600 eggs and about 80% hatch! If the collected eggs are placed in an open container they should hatch after 4 months. No special attention is required during this time.

Nymphs

Usually the nymph manages to free itself completely from the eggshell. However, sometimes it is retained on the insect's body. An eggshell which is attached to the abdomen must be removed if the insect

1. INDIAN *(Carausius morosus)*

egg
length 2mm

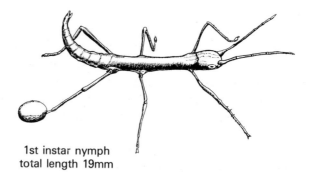

1st instar nymph
total length 19mm

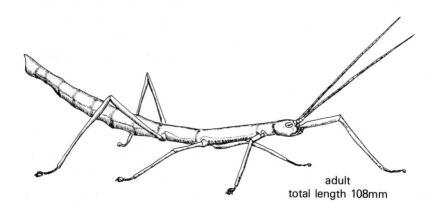

adult
total length 108mm

fig 6

is to survive. Assistance can be given by holding the eggshell between one's thumb and forefinger. The insect will pull until its abdomen is free and one can actually feel the force which is being exerted. An examination of the empty eggshell reveals that it consists of a hard, brown, outer chorion and an inner white soft sac.

The eggshell is of no use to the insect once it has hatched. If it is attached to a leg then it is best left; if an attempt is made to remove the eggshell there is a risk of the insect discarding the leg. The nymph plods around dragging the eggshell like a 'ball and chain'. Not surprisingly, the insect tries to free itself as quickly as possible by trapping the eggshell in a crevice and then attempting to pull its leg free. This is usually successful and the eggshell is lost within a few days; if not, the insect is free after the first ecdysis because the eggshell remains attached to the old skin which is shed.

A newly hatched nymph is dark brown and can be seen plodding along with the tip of its abdomen curled up. When alarmed, the insect may either walk faster or else it clamps all its legs alongside its body and falls to the ground looking like a straight stick.

The Indian stick insect grows by climbing out of its skin six times during a period of five months. The shed skin is usually eaten immediately after ecdysis.

Larger nymphs are usually green and can be well camouflaged. They hang vertically when resting and sometimes suspend themselves from a sprig of privet by using just their front two feet.

If alarmed, they will readily drop to the ground as straight 'sticks'. Some individuals then extend a middle leg and use this to kick off potential predators. In the wild, these stick insects have been observed to deter wasps in this way. The nymphs have another defence mechanism of releasing a few drops of fluid from their mouths. This liquid is orange-brown in colour and has a pungent smell. It is designed to be unpleasant rather than harmful.

Adults

When an Indian stick insect becomes an adult (108mm total length) it is usually bright green in colour. However, as the new skin hardens it becomes duller. Other individuals may be various shades such as light brown or dark grey. Darkly coloured insects often have a pale diamond shaped patch on their abdomen. The colour of the insect is partly affected by external influences such as the quality and type of foodplant, temperature, and light intensity. For example, Indian stick insects apparently go darker in colour at night. Stick insects may also darken as they grow older.

The adults can be well camouflaged although in captivity they appear to reject resting on the privet in favour of grouping high up on the ventilated sides of the cage—where they are very conspicuous! All adults have red tips to the tops of their front legs. This is probably a form of defence in that the red colouration may startle predators. Alternatively, when alarmed, the adults can show the same defences as the nymphs; they can drop to the ground as 'sticks' or else release some fluid from their mouths.

It is possible to demonstrate an adult Indian stick insect falling into and out of a 'stick' by following the procedure below (see **fig 7**). The insect can be held upside-down between its second and third pairs of legs with the thumb and forefinger of one hand. Using the other hand, the first and second pairs of legs can be guided forwards alongside the insect's body and the back legs guided backwards (diag 1). Within a few seconds the insect should assume a 'stick' posture, and can be rolled over in this state (diag 2). The insect will spring to life again if it is placed the right way up and gently tickled about 2cm from the tip of its abdomen (diag 3).

About two weeks after becoming an adult, the insect will start to lay eggs. These are dropped on to the floor of the cage. Indian stick insects are parthenogenetic. Several eggs are laid every day over a period of seven months; some insects reaching a grand total of over 700 eggs!

Although this species is parthenogenetic, males do occasionally occur. This is a rare event but the probability of this happening is unknown; estimates range from 1 male per 1,000 females, to 1 male per 10,000! The adult male is smaller (82mm total length) and thinner. He is light brown but his thorax is coloured differently; the underside is red and there are two sloping red marks on the upperside. A male Indian stick insect is hyperactive and does not live as long as the female. These insects probably do mate despite the fact that the female can reproduce without a male.

Adult male
and female
C.morosus

Regenerated leg on head of *S.sipylus*

Eggs (from left to right, top row: *E.calcarata, S.sipylus, C.morosus, Baculum TH U1* bottom row: *B.rossius, O.macklottii, E.tiaratum*).

A.maculata stick insect eating.

S.sipylus adult showing pink wings.

Adult male and female *E.calcarata* drinking.

Adult *E.tiaratum* female showing white spermatophore.

'In-cage' — cage suitable for stick insects.

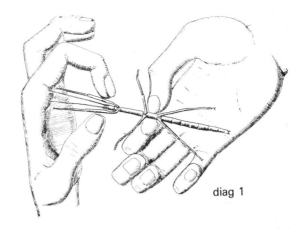

diag 1

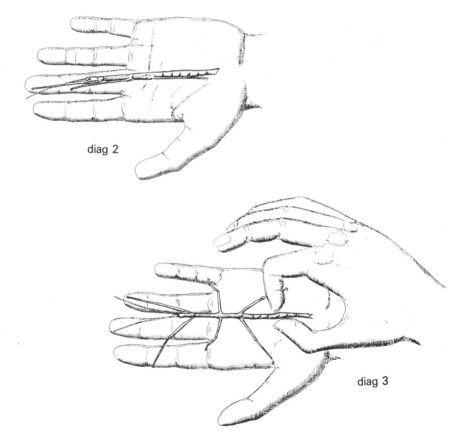

diag 2

diag 3

fig 7

29

2. PINK WINGED *(Sipyloidea sipylus)*

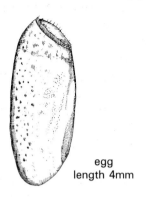

egg
length 4mm

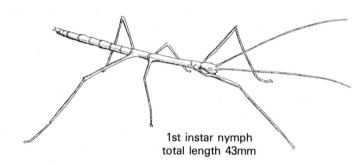

1st instar nymph
total length 43mm

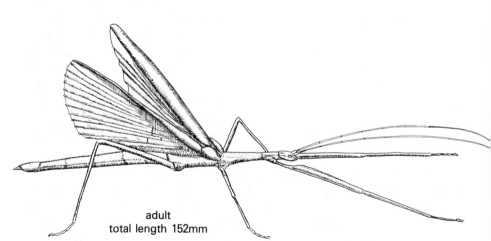

adult
total length 152mm

fig 8

These stick insects are pretty; the first instar nymph being delicate and pale green, whilst the adult is straw coloured and has large pink wings. If the surroundings are very warm the adult can fly over a short distance, for example across a room. When inside the cage the adult insect may flash its wings. This always happens with insects that have just acquired their wings after the final ecdysis. The insects eat bramble leaves but if adults are present the cage should not be completely packed with food. Instead, plenty of space should be left so that if an adult flashes its wings there is less risk of a wing being caught on a bramble thorn and ripped. Other suitable foodplants include raspberry and the houseplant maranta.

The Pink winged stick insect originated in East Asia but is also found in Madagascar, East Indies, and Australia. These insects are reasonably hardy and are being kept in schools with much success.

An advantage of keeping this species is that one does not have to spend time sorting the eggs from the frass—this is because the adults glue the eggs around the cage! This behaviour is unique among the species described in this book.

Eggs

The egg is mottled grey in colour and is rough in texture. It is elongated and about 4mm long. The 'base' of the egg runs down its entire length and it is this area which can be glued to various objects. *The egg should not be removed from where it has been glued.* Typical places include; in curled pieces of leaf, between folds in the paper lining in the base of the cage, and in the holes of the aluminium ventilation panels. In order to avoid the cage becoming cluttered with eggs a more attractive surface can be presented to the adults. The cardboard from egg-boxes (packaging for half a dozen eggs, obtained from markets) provides an ideal surface and so pieces of this can be put into the cage when adults are there. Occasionally an egg is glued in a seemingly unlikely place like the leg, antenna, or wing of another stick insect! In such cases, the recipient does not appear to object and these eggs have been observed to hatch in due course.

Sometimes adults cram many eggs into one place. This usually results in the later eggs partly covering the opercula of earlier ones. If the operculum can not be pushed off completely, the opening is not large enough for the insect to climb out of its eggshell. A nymph trapped like this is unable to emerge fully and usually dies the next day.

Pink winged eggs hatch after three months. They require no

attention during their incubation.

Nymphs

A newly emerged nymph is not encumbered by its empty eggshell because the eggshell remains fixed to where it was glued. The young nymph is light green and is relatively large for a first instar stick insect. It walks in a very dainty manner. The insect is fragile and the area where the thorax joins the abdomen is particularly vulnerable. If this is damaged, for example by a fall, the whole abdomen droops downwards and the insect will soon die.

The nymphs distribute themselves around the cage and rest quite separately from each other. The preferred resting places are the vertical sides of the cage. However these areas are usually already occupied by older nymphs or adults and, as these insects have priority, the younger insects are forced to seek out alternative sites on which to rest. The young nymphs choose the next best place which is underneath the roof. They tend to space out regularly over the area available. The more insects there are, the closer is the spacing.

It is a good idea to mix larger Pink winged stick insects with the very young nymphs because *newly hatched nymphs are reluctant to feed unless there are older insects present.*

As the nymph grows, it loses its green colouration and usually turns a straw colour. (Except in the late spring when the older nymphs usually stay green, probably as a result of eating new young bramble leaves.)

The nymph has several ways of defending itself. It can stay still and rely on camouflage. Or it might clamp all its legs beside its body and drop the ground as a 'stick'. Alternatively, it might secrete a few drops of brown defensive fluid from its mouth. In any case the Pink winged stick will probably release its defensive odour; this is quite a powerful musky smell which clings to one's fingers.

Only the adult insect has wings, but their development is occurring throughout the nymphal stages. This is shown by the presence of wingbuds on the thorax.

Adults

Immediately after the last ecdysis (which may take 1 ½ hours), the adult insect moves round to an upright position beside its skin. At this time its wings are two cream coloured shrivelled masses (about 1cm long) at the top of the thorax.

The insect has to pump blood into these wings in order to make them expand to their full length of 5cm. This process lasts about 30 minutes. When the wings are fully expanded, they are white and should hang down the body of the insect, splaying at the end, looking like a long white petticoat. Occasionally the insect does not do this properly and so twisted useless wings result. An insect which has succeeded in pumping out its wings will later fold one wing on top of the other so that they align with its body. The wings turn pink during the next few days. The adult is quite weak at this stage and therefore delays flying for a week or so. After this time a red patch may appear on the thorax between the wings.

When the insect is ready to fly it sometimes walks out of the cage as soon as the door is opened. The insect will take off if placed on one's outstretched palm. It is obvious when the adult is preparing to take off because its middle leg twitches to and from its body several times. One can encourage the insect to fly by gently blowing on it (see **fig 9**).

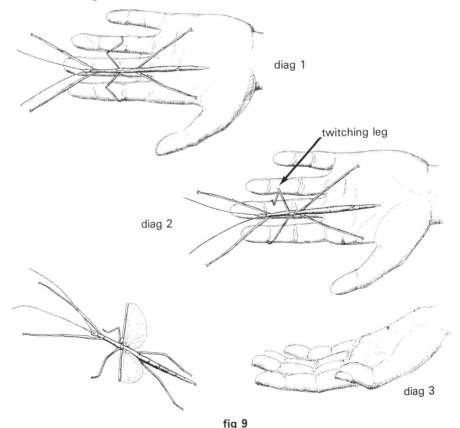

diag 1

twitching leg

diag 2

diag 3

fig 9

The adult flies gracefully across the room, maintaining roughly the same altitude. A short resting period follows which enables one to pick up an insect from where it has landed. The insect will usually make two or three flights in any one session. The longest flights are made by the younger adults, probably because these insects have bodies which are not as heavily laden with eggs as the older adults.

The wings are also used as one of the defence mechanisms of this stick insect. If it is not warm enough for the insect to actually fly away from danger, the wings are flashed in order to startle the potential enemy. It is possible to make a Pink winged adult show its wings by gently squeezing the abdomen about 4cm from the tip.

This type of stick insect does not hesitate to hit out at anything that disturbs it. If someone accidentally knocks an insect, it usually responds by hitting that person's hand with a back leg! In addition to these defences, the adult retains all the defences it had as a nymph.

The Pink winged stick insect lives for about one year, of which seven months are devoted to laying eggs. About 100 eggs are laid altogether which is quite low compared with the number of eggs laid by some other species of stick insect. However, it is difficult to record the numbers of eggs accurately because they are glued all over the cage and should not be detached. The insect takes great care in selecting a suitable site on which to lay an egg. The tip of the abdomen is covered with sensory hairs and the adult spends several minutes exploring a potentially suitable surface with this end of its body. Only one or two eggs are laid at a time and so this whole process must be repeated again and again in the course of the following months. Egg-laying can sometimes be observed in the daytime but usually occurs at night.

In the dark, the body of the adult remains straw-coloured. However, the colour of the compound eyes changes from being clear with a small black centre to becoming completely black.

As the insect grows older, its body becomes darker, acquiring a deep shade of pink.

3. THAILAND *(Baculum TH U1)*

egg
length 4mm

1st instar nymph
total length 27mm

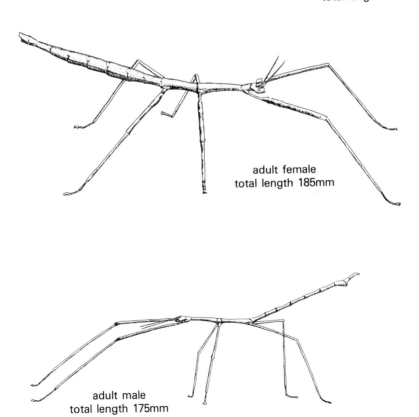

adult female
total length 185mm

adult male
total length 175mm

fig 10

These insects are very stick-like and can be really well camouflaged amongst their foodplant of bramble or raspberry. The adult male is especially active and is well worth watching because he is so slender and walks in such a dainty way. The adult female lays over 700 eggs, many of which will hatch. This makes her the most prolific stick insect discussed in this book.

This is one of the easiest species to keep but the insects must be handled carefully as they have a tendency to lose legs.

Thailand stick insects are relatively long-lived, their lifespan being about 14 months.

Eggs

The egg is light brown, 4mm long, and flat. A good method of collecting the egg is by using an artist's paintbrush to separate them from the frass. They can then be gathered up and placed in an open container. It is advisable *not* to save all the eggs; otherwise there will soon be far too many insects to cope with. The eggs hatch in approximately two months, but in summer this period is shorter, sometimes being only four weeks.

Nymphs

A newly hatched nymph sometimes retains its old eggshell on one or more of its legs. The eggshell should not be tampered with because the insect will lose it in due course. Thailand nymphs usually group on the ends of the foodplant rather than on the sides of the cage. Camouflage appears to be the only method of defence for these insects.

Unfortunately Thailand nymphs are fragile and have a tendency to lose legs. This is not disastrous because the insect can regenerate several new legs but nevertheless the handling of these insects should be minimized. If handling is unavoidable, for example during the weekly clean-out of the cage, measures can be taken to reduce the risk of damaging the insects and these will now be outlined.

When a jar containing fresh bramble leaves is placed into the cage, the jar holding the old food can be left in. During the next few days most of the insects that were clustered on the old food will move over onto the fresh food. This means that when the jar of old bramble is finally removed, there are only a few insects that need to be picked off and returned to the cage. One way of transferring the smaller insects is to blow them off the food into one's cupped hand and then toss them quickly into the cage. The insects are not damaged by this action because they have the ability to fall over several metres and still land safely on their feet. Young nymphs that have dropped off the food and are on a horizontal surface can be moved on the tip of an artist's paintbrush. An older insect can be picked up by its abdomen, a short distance from the tip, and placed on the side of the cage.

There are two sexes of Thailand stick insect. A medium-sized nymph can be sexed by looking under the tip of its abdomen — a male will have a 'bump'. As the nymphs grow larger, the difference between the sexes becomes more apparent because the males are much thinner than the females. In addition, the males appear to develop at a much faster rate. This may be an attempt to prevent in-breeding between insects of the same stock. Nevertheless in captivity in-breeding does occur because females which have hatched from older eggs mature at the same time as males which have emerged from later eggs.

Adults

The body of the adult female may be fawn, green, or brown. Individuals do not change in colour, with the exception of becoming darker as they age. Often, the legs have yellow/brown stripes but these are absent on regenerated limbs. In addition, there are many small leaf-like protuberances on the legs. The head of the female has two 'ear-like' growths (see **fig 11**).

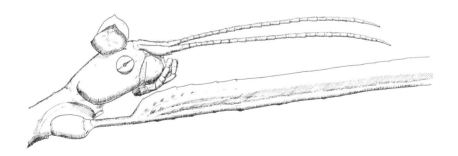

fig 11

37

Her main defence is that of camouflage. When disturbed, she adopts a rigid stance with all her legs splayed out.

The male is smaller and slenderer than the female. He is purple/brown in colour and has yellow eyes. When there are too many males in one place their 'knees' turn black. Again, camouflage is the main defence. However, if a male is disturbed he readily walks away. When he reaches the edge of the object he is walking on, he waves his front two legs up and down. These insects will mate about a couple of weeks after becoming adults. This occurs either during the day or night. The male usually climbs on top of the female and curls the tip of his abdomen underneath hers. Mating typically lasts for a few hours and does not prevent the female from walking about or even eating. The males appear to live as long as the females and mating occurs frequently during the rest of their lives. However these insects do not pair up for life; the adult female having several partners.

The Thailand female produces about 700 eggs over ten months. The number of eggs laid per day can fluctuate between zero and eleven. Each egg is catapulted over a distance of many centimetres and if one lands on a solid surface, the noise of the impact can be heard. Sometimes a female will lay an egg whenever the cage door is opened.

The adults are not as delicate as the nymphs but should still be handled with care.

4. MACLEAYS SPECTRE *(Extatosoma tiaratum)*

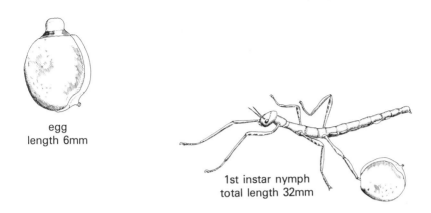

egg
length 6mm

1st instar nymph
total length 32mm

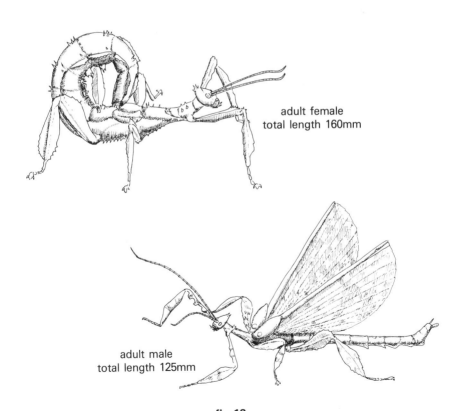

adult female
total length 160mm

adult male
total length 125mm

fig 12

These stick insects, which come from Australia, look quite bizarre. Instead of being long and thin, they are bulky and have leafy-looking legs. In addition, they usually have their abdomens curled up—a stance which causes many people to believe, mistakenly, that Australian stick insects are scorpions. However, despite resembling scorpions in this respect, the stick insects are harmless.

The nymph and adult stages are particularly resilient to being handled, making these insects ideal for school use.

One point that should be remembered with this species is that because the insects are so bulky they have large appetites! It is therefore necessary to give them more bramble leaves than are required by most other types of stick insect.

Eggs

The egg is relatively large, being about 6mm long. It is shiny, hard and round. Unlike many other types of stick insect egg which are dark in colour, the eggs of this species are conspicuous because of their cream and brown markings. As a result of the above characteristics, it is easy to collect Australian eggs because they can be picked up by hand from the frass. The sorted eggs should be placed on some dry sand, inside a container which is then closed.

Hatching these eggs can present problems and many people experience difficulties. This is because Australian stick insect eggs will probably *not* hatch if they are just left indoors. Instead, it appears that they require additional heat for them to develop properly. This extra warmth may be achieved by placing the container of eggs in a warm place; for example above a radiator or in an airing cupboard.

Some people recommend spraying the eggs very lightly with water. If this is done, the eggs should be inspected regularly to make sure that mould is not developing.

If the above conditions are satisfied, the eggs should start hatching after about eight months. However, the proportion of eggs which hatch is relatively low, being much less than half.

Nymphs

Unlike most other species of stick insect, Australian eggs hatch during the day. When an Australian nymph hatches it is extremely active. It curls its abdomen up and runs round and round the container in which it is housed. The nymph is black and has an orange head. Sometimes the eggshell is retained on a leg—in which case the noise of the hard eggshell banging against the container will soon be heard! The eggshell is lost as soon as the insect is placed in its new surroundings.

The nymph does best if it is reared under a clear plastic basin, about 15cm high. The basin should be inverted to cover moist bramble leaves which have been placed on a sheet of paper. The food should be replenished daily. The nymphs can live in the basin until a few days after their second ecdysis when they can be transferred to a standard size cage.

Large nymphs are golden brown or dark grey and continue to curl their abdomens up. There are male and female insects and it is possible to sex the nymphs by using the fact that the male has prominent wingbuds on his thorax.

The insects rest separately on the ventilated sides of the cage or else on the foodplant which is rapidly being devoured! The nymphs are usually found in pairs of one male and one female (although of course mating cannot occur at this stage.)

It is easy to handle these insects because they are very resilient and rarely lose legs. However, they frequently release their pungent defensive odour. When alarmed, young nymphs sometimes drop to the ground. However, unlike some other types of stick insect which fall as straight 'sticks', Australian nymphs keep their legs bent. The insects remain in this state, motionless, until the danger has passed.

Despite the complex shape of these Australian insects, they usually climb out of their skins with no difficulty. Furthermore, they do not always eat their discarded skins and so this provides an ideal opportunity to look at a skin more closely.

The nymphs develop quickly, achieving an adult status within four months of hatching. Immediately after the final moult, the insect is bright yellow. However, the cuticle soon changs to a light brown colour.

Adults

The adult female can be golden brown or grey. She is very bulky and can achieve a weight of 15g (this is 10× heavier than the adult Indian stick insect.) She now has many spines all over her body. Many are on the underside of the abdomen and these help to protect it when it is curled up. There are even spines 'sprouting' from the top of her head which is shaped like a cone. On her thorax there are two small brown wing coverings but no actual wings.

In contrast the male has large functional wings. At rest, the wings are folded down the thorax and also along the entire length of the abdomen. The presence of these wings means that although the male nymphs curl their abdomens up, fully grown males cannot adopt this posture. The wings are mainly clear but have a pattern of black markings on them. The male readily flies when given the opportunity and can achieve a strong sustained flight across a room. The noise of his beating wings can be heard easily. The adult male is smaller and slenderer than the female. He is usually a mottled dark grey colour and has spiny legs.

A few weeks after becoming adults, the insects will be ready to mate. It is likely that the male will have been waiting for a female because, as with other types of sexual stick insects, males appear to reach maturity earlier than the females. The male will climb on top of the female and mating will last for several hours. Mating takes place on many occasions throughout the lives of the insects and, as a consequence, their leafy-looking legs may become increasingly punctured by each other's spines! After mating, the male usually remains on the female for a while before moving away. The spermatophore, which can be white or pink, remains attached to the female for several hours and is clearly visible (see photo in centre pages). Later, it drops off.

The abdomen of the adult female swells when she is ready to lay eggs. A few eggs are catapulted every day for several months.

The adults can firmly hold onto a surface with their claws and this means that patience is needed when persuading the insects to relinquish their grip. The defensive odour is readily released.

5. JAVANESE *(Orxines macklottii)*

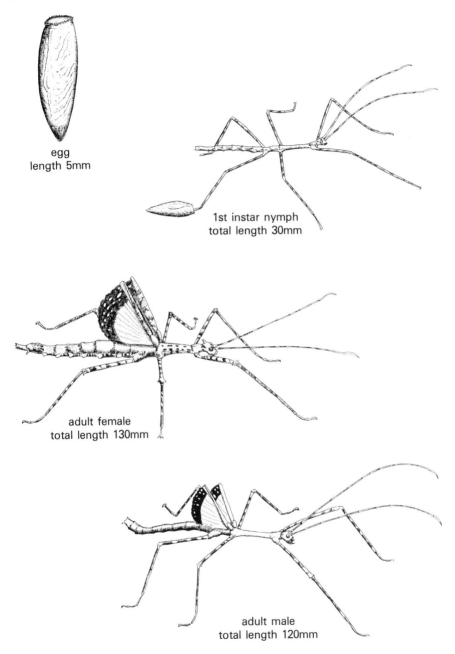

egg
length 5mm

1st instar nymph
total length 30mm

adult female
total length 130mm

adult male
total length 120mm

fig 13

These are very attractive insects. When adult, they are mossy coloured and have bright orange wings with black and white borders. Care must be taken with these insects to ensure that they are shielded from draughts. This can be achieved by enclosing a ventilated cage within a clear container, for example a balance case. The insects eat rhododendron leaves and these should be sprayed daily with water.

Eggs

The egg is brown, torpedo-shaped, and 5mm long. Each egg is buried in dry sand. It is very easy to separate the eggs from the sand by using a strainer. The sieved sand can be returned to the cage. If the loose eggs are stored in a closed container indoors, they should start to hatch after about five months.

Nymphs

The speckled green and brown nymph has relatively long legs and antennae. Like the young Pink winged nymph it walks in a dainty manner. Sometimes the eggshell is retained on one or more of the insect's legs. If this happens no attempt should be made to remove it because the insect will lose it in due course.

The newly emerged insect appears reluctant to feed if there are no older insects present. If this is the situation, moist shredded leaves should be provided. A rhododendron leaf can be suitably cut up by placing it in a liquidiser containing a small amount of water and running at maximum speed for five seconds. The end product can be put on a saucer and the excess water drained off. This saucer holding the food can be placed in the cage. Fortunately, this procedure does not have to be followed for very long because after a few days the insect appears to be able to eat part of a whole rhododendron leaf.

The nymphs group together, either on the foodplant or on the sides of the cage. When larger insects are present they often form an elaborate matrix. This mass may be suspended from just a few insects which are holding on to an object high up in the cage. Such behaviour can present a problem when the foodplant is being replenished because the insects at the top of the chain may let go when they are disturbed. The whole cluster of insects then falls to the ground in a heap which quickly untangles and disperses! During all of this the insects are likely to release their defensive odour which has a very pungent smell.

There are male and female Javanese insects but it is difficult to sex them when they are young. The most obvious difference is that the male is more slender than the female. Both sexes cling tenaciously to one's fingers.

Adults

The adult is a mixture of speckled green, brown, and cream in colour. In addition both sexes have small, predominantly orange wings. These are not large enough to enable the insects to fly—instead their purpose is for defence. In the wild the wings are flashed at potential predators in order to startle them.

When the insect has just completed its final moult, it is pale and has its wings concertinad up. These wings are slowly pumped out and are usually fully extended within half an hour. However it takes a few days for them to acquire their true orange, black and white colouration.

The adult Javanese female can be persuaded to unfold her wings if she is gently squeezed midway along her abdomen. The male, however, is much more reluctant to show his wings.

The adults can be quite active. Their method of walking usually arouses interest because as the insects move they make exaggerated swaying movements from side to side. Presumably this disco-dancer action is used because it imitates a twig blowing in the wind.

It is sometimes tricky handling these insects because they can jump. This ability is not well developed—it is negligible when compared with that of a grasshopper—but it does mean that the insect is likely to topple off one's hand or off the table. The surrounding surfaces should be clear or else accidents may happen; for example, it has been known for a Javanese adult to jump into a mug of steaming coffee.

When these insects are disturbed, their pungent defensive odour is very apparent. If the adults are very alarmed, they release a small amount of yellow fluid from their mouths.

After being handled, it is likely that the insect will clean its antennae. Each long antenna is passed slowly through the mouth of the insect and withdrawn again with the assistance of the front legs.

Mating occurs a few weeks after the insects have become adults. The male climbs on top of the female and starts to mate. Sometimes several pairs will be mating while they are hanging in the matrix formation described earlier. If they are disturbed, the insects will walk away, usually still coupled.

The female buries her eggs and so a small container holding dry sand, about 5cm deep, should be placed on the cage floor. She will carefully bury one egg at a time. Her body sways from side to side as she pushes her abdomen into the sand and releases an egg. She then brings her abdomen up to the surface and, using her ovipositor, flicks some sand to ensure that the egg is covered.

6. CORSICAN *(Bacillus rossius)*

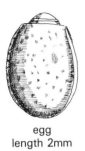

egg
length 2mm

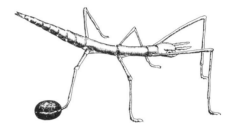

1st instar nymph
total length 22mm

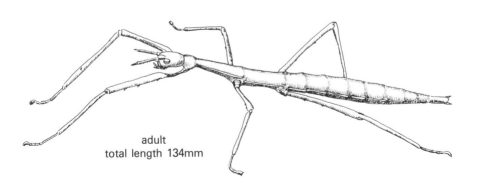

adult
total length 134mm

fig 14

Corsican stick insects are vividly coloured and have two conspicuous stripes running down each side of their bodies. The adults show a range of colours; some insects are bright green with white or red stripes, whilst others are pink with red stripes.

This species was discovered as early as 1790. The preferred foodplant is rose leaves but, of course, the leaves must not be collected from garden roses which have been sprayed with insecticide. Bramble and raspberry leaves are also eaten.

These insects can be difficult to rear because when they are medium-sized they often die for no apparent reason.

Eggs

The egg is round, black, pitted, and 2mm long. An easy way of collecting the eggs is to remove and tilt the paper lining the base of the cage: a gentle tap encourages the eggs to roll off. The eggs can be caught in a dish and stored indoors. It is best to save most of the eggs because so many of the nymphs die. After five months the eggs should start hatching. When the eggs are due to hatch, it is advisable to put a lid on top of the container holding them. This simple action reduces the loss of moisture and successful hatching is then much more likely to occur. If the container is left open, some insects will only manage to pull their head and thorax out of the eggshell. These insects are doomed to die in a day or two.

Nymphs

The newly emerged nymph is bright green. It is an active insect and is quite tenacious. Sometimes the eggshell is retained on one or more of the legs but usually the insect manages to discard it within a few hours. The young nymph will sometimes pause and wave its front two legs up and down.

Very young nymphs do well if they are kept under a clear plastic basin — as described in Section 4, Macleays Spectre stick insects.

As the nymph grows older, it may remain bright green or change to a fawn or pink colour. This colour variation makes a collection of Corsican stick insects look especially interesting. During the day, the nymphs rest separately either around the cage, usually on the ventilated sides, or on the foodplant.

Camouflage appears to be the main method of defence. However, an insect which is very alarmed releases some green defensive fluid from its mouth.

Adults

The adult is particularly attractive because this is the stage when the contrasting coloured stripes on its body become obvious. In addition, the adult has red tops to its front legs and sometimes has small black spikes under its middle and back legs.

Like the nymphs, the adults rest separately from each other. When disturbed, they walk away and, on reaching the edge of a surface, wave their front two legs up and down. The defensive fluid is rarely released.

This species is parthenogenetic and, about two weeks after the insect becomes an adult, egg-laying commences. Eggs are catapulted to the ground over the next seven months; the horizontal distance over which an egg is catapulted can be as great as 30cm. About 300 eggs are laid altogether.

7. NEW GUINEA *(Eurycantha calcarata)*

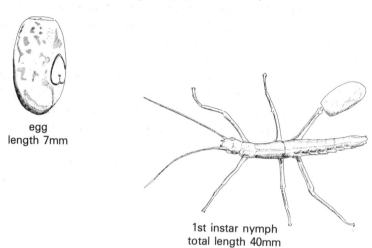

egg
length 7mm

1st instar nymph
total length 40mm

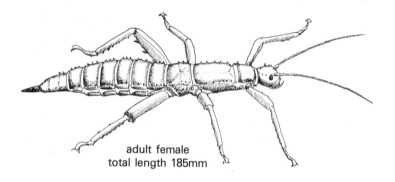

adult female
total length 185mm

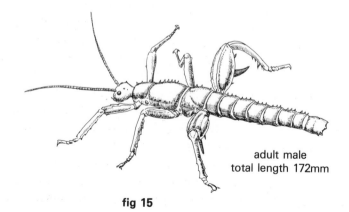

adult male
total length 172mm

fig 15

These insects look incredible because they are so powerfully built. Adults appear the most impressive because their bodies seem to be armour-plated! They are huge, broad, and glossy dark brown. Their sheer width causes many people to say, jokingly, that these insects should be called 'log insects' rather than 'stick insects'.

It is difficult to see New Guinea stick insects in the cage as they deliberately crawl under cover whenever possible. One sheltered area can harbour many large insects because they pile on top of one another. It is quite common to find all the large nymphs and adults packed together in one place.

New Guinea stick insects eat bramble or raspberry leaves. The adults require additional water. Both sexes are relatively long-lived, achieving lifespans of about 18 months.

Eggs

The egg is large, being 7mm long. It is tubular and mottled grey in colour. Each egg is buried in sand and so can be collected easily by sieving the sand through a strainer. If one wishes to continue keeping this species it is advisable to save all the eggs because the proportion that hatch appears to be relatively low. The eggs take six months to hatch if they are left in an open container indoors.

Nymphs

The newly emerged nymph is dark grey in colour. Initially the eggshell may be retained but it is usually lost within a few hours. The insect can move quite quickly but when disturbed immediately flattens itself against the surface on which it has been walking.

The young nymphs should be reared under basins—as already described in Section 4, Macleays Spectre insects.

A young insect usually rests by pressing itself against a bramble stem or, if other stick insects are resting vertically, against one of them. When the nymph is medium-sized, it starts to seek out horizontal places in which to rest. Such an insect will instinctively crawl underneath an overhanging object. If none is available, the insect makes its own shelter by biting off bramble leaves so that they fall to the base of the cage. A more satisfactory arrangement is achieved if one deliberately creates a hiding place; for example by providing a fold of paper for the insect to crawl under. This can be done by lining the base of the cage with a piece of paper 10cm longer than usual and folding the excess back onto itself, the flap being uppermost. The insects appear to rest underneath the paper for most of the day. However, when a skin-change is imminent, a nymph will abandon this sheltered resting place in favour of an exposed vertical position much higher up in the cage. Here, the nymph will pause for many minutes before beginning to moult. The other New Guinea stick insects in the cage remain underneath the paper and so the moulting insect does not have the protection of a nearby insect.

Having completed the skin-change, the insect remains in the open for several hours, allowing its new skin to harden and darken. Large nymphs can vary in colour; some are a mottled green and others are fawn. The skin of a New Guinea stick insect is particularly interesting to examine because of its width. For example, details such as the slit along the top of the thorax, and how the breathing tubes connect with the body, can be seen clearly.

It is easy to sex a nymph by looking at the tip of the abdomen; that of the male is blunted whereas the female's is pointed because of her developing ovipositor.

Adults

When a nymph has completed its final moult, the new cuticle requires several days to darken fully. The male exhibits the most dramatic colour change because he turns a rich glossy dark brown. He has also acquired an impressive 1cm long spike on the underside of each of his powerful thick back thighs. These spikes can be used to defend the insect. If alarmed, the male lifts his abdomen up and straddles his back legs in the air to display his spikes. At the same time he can release a defensive odour. If provoked further, the adult may hiss. This can be followed by the adult attempting to stab the spikes, present on the underside of the back legs, into the intruder. These defences mean that although New Guinea adults can be handled they should not be teased.

The female is usually mid-brown in colour. She has numerous short spikes but, unlike the male, no large ones. She shows all the defence mechanisms found in the male but because her spines are shorter she is less dangerous. At the tip of her abdomen there is a long ovipositor, 15mm in length.

Mating occurs several weeks after the insects are fully grown. The male climbs on top of the female and curls the tip of his abdomen underneath hers. It is not common to see these insects mating during the day. However, if they are taken on a car journey, the motion experienced during travelling appears to prompt them into mating shortly afterwards.

When the female is ready to start laying eggs, her abdomen swells to a thickness of about 2cm. It is at this stage that a container holding dry sand, about 5cm deep, should be placed in the cage, near one of the sides. The female will usually support herself on the side of the cage with her ovipositor resting on the sand. She then sways her abdomen from side to side and gently pushes her ovipositor into the sand. During the next minute she releases an egg. She then withdraws her ovipositor and uses it to make short sweeping movements which flick sand to level the depression that she has made. Sometimes females deposit eggs in crevices. When out of the cage, the insects have been seen to lay eggs in: the fold of a jumper, a long-haired rug, and between one's fingers! The adult follows the same procedure regardless of where she is laying the egg and this means that sometimes her behaviour is inappropriate. For example, if she has laid an egg between one's fingers, she will still try to bury it by making short flicking movements across the hand.

Unlike many other types of stick insect, the New Guinea female does not lay several eggs each day. Instead she fluctuates between periods of producing no eggs and those of intense egg-laying activity. After weeks of laying no eggs she may suddenly bury as many as thirty-nine in one day!

During the day, male and female adults rest, under cover, on the paper lining the base of the cage. Every week when the cage is cleaned out, this paper (complete with insects resting on it), is removed. This provides an ideal opportunity to give the adults their extra water. Saucers of water can be placed on a table and the insects positioned so that their mouthparts are immersed (see photo in centre pages). Drinking will take place for the next hour or two and the adults should not be disturbed during this time. After they have finished they will walk away, their bodies now swollen. Usually this weekly drinking session is sufficient for the insects. However, if the surroundings are particularly warm, more water may be required. This need will be indicated by the insects exercising their mouthparts and roaming continuously around the cage. This noisy churning will only cease when they receive some water.

chapter 5

Suggested projects

Probably the best way of learning about anything is by direct observation. Many observations can be made as one looks after stick insects—for example, it is common to witness the insects feeding, laying eggs, and cleaning their antennae. Other observations can be recorded if particular projects are carried out. Five projects are suggested below but there is scope for many more. None of the projects described will harm the stick insects.

One advantage of finding out about stick insects is that sometimes this knowledge applies to insects in general as well as to stick insects. For example, one can observe a stick insect climb out of its skin—but how many people realise that *all* insects grow like this?

Project 1

INSECT STRUCTURE

An adult stick insect can be drawn and the illustration labelled (see **fig 1**). This basic design is representative of all insects.

The texture of the cuticle can be seen if the insect is placed under a microscope (low magnification). Details of other structures, such as compound eyes, are also revealed.

The size of the adult can be measured and the variation between individuals established. The results can be kept for several generations to see if the average body length increases.

A 'beauty contest' may be held and a vote taken for the healthiest stick insect.

Project 2

WALKING

Stick insects have six legs but in what order are they moved? This can be found out by two people watching a stick insect which is walking. An adult insect should be selected and each of its legs assigned a number. Initially, one person chooses to watch one leg whilst the partner watches another leg. The idea is for each person to shout out the number of the leg they are observing whenever it touches the ground. If the stick insect falters, it can be encouraged to continue walking if it is gently blown on. The results can be recorded using a tape recorder. The method can then be repeated with a different pair of legs. When several combinations have been recorded the order in which the legs are moved can be established.

Other details about the walking behaviour of stick insects can be recorded on a blackened piece of glass. A large piece of glass or aluminium (approx 60cm × 30cm) can be moved across the top of a candle flame and blackened by the smoke. The area should be blackened as evenly as possible. When the glass has cooled down an adult stick insect can be placed on it. The insect will make tracks on the blackened area. Distances between marks made by the same foot can be measured to give the average stride of the insect. This method can be repeated with adults from other species to see if there is a relationship between size of leg and length of stride. Other observations such as whether the insect drags its feet and abdomen can also be noted.

Project 3

DIET

The staple diets of stick insects have already been given but there are many other plants which are suitable as food. However, insects from different species eat different leaves and so it is best to do this project with a cage containing only one species of stick insect. A jar containing sprigs of the standard acceptable foodplant can be placed in the cage. Then another jar holding leaves from different plants can be added. These plants should have whole leaves. The jars can be left in the cage for a few days and then the plants examined to see which leaves have been nibbled. This procedure can be repeated, presenting the stick insects with different plants until one is sampled. More leaves of this accepted foodplant can then be collected and put in a cage containing another variety of stick insect to see if this food is acceptable to those insects as well. So far, leaves which have been eaten by at least one type of stick insect include: hawthorn, oak, geranium, chrysanthemum, buddleia, and beech.

Project 4

GROWTH CHARTS

The growth of a stick insect can be recorded on a piece of graph paper. The y-axis should represent the insect's body length (i.e. from head to tip of abdomen), and the x-axis the age, in weeks, of the insect. A stick insect should be selected as soon as it hatches and its length plotted for week zero. This measurement can be repeated at weekly intervals until the stick insect is an adult. This project lasts for about 4-5 months. The completed growth chart clearly shows the dramatic increase in size of the insect following each skin-change. The procedure can be repeated with stick insects from other species and can be used to find out if the number of times a stick insect sheds its skin depends on which species it is from. Growth charts from stick insects can be compared with those obtained from other insects such as caterpillars.

Project 5

EGG-LAYING CHARTS

A female stick insect can be put into a separate cage a few days after she has become an adult. If she is from a species which reproduces sexually then an adult male should be placed in the same cage. Every day the eggs which have been laid can be counted and removed from the cage. This information can be shown on a graph; the y-axis showing the number of eggs laid per day and the x-axis time (in days). After about seven months the egg-laying chart will be finished. The chart shows the variation in the number of eggs laid per day, whether or not there is a gradual build up in the number of eggs laid, and the total number of eggs produced. This project can be repeated with adults from different types of stick insect to ascertain what variations exist between species. It is not recommended to use a Pink winged adult in this project because this insect glues its eggs all over the cage—making them hard to find and difficult to remove.

Stockist of stick insects, cages, and this book.

Small-Life Supplies,
9 Upton Avenue,
Cheadle Hulme,
Cheshire SK8 7HX.
ENGLAND.
Tel: 061-485 2289.

New address from Aug 1989:
SMALL-LIFE SUPPLIES,
Normanton Lane Industrial Estate,
Bottesford, Nottingham,
NG13 0EN. ENGLAND.
Tel: 0949 42446

Acknowledgements

I'm grateful to J.E., K.L., and B. for their helpful comments during the preparation of this book. I'd also like to thank Dr. J. T. Sellick for the encouragement he gave me many years ago when my interest in stick insects began.

Index